G000114070

52 THINGS TO DOODLE
WHILE YOU POO

AN HACHETTE UK COMPANY
WWW.HACHETTE.CO.UK

SUMMERSDALE PUBLISHERS LTD
PART OF OCTOPUS PUBLISHING GROUP LIMITED
CARMELITE HOUSE
50 VICTORIA EMBANKMENT
LONDON
EC4Y 0DZ
UK

WWW.SUMMERSDALE.COM
PRINTED AND BOUND IN MALTA
ISBN: 978-1-78685-764-4

SUBSTANTIAL DISCOUNTS ON BULK QUANTITIES OF SUMMERSDALE BOOKS ARE AVAILABLE
TO CORPORATIONS, PROFESSIONAL ASSOCIATIONS AND OTHER ORGANISATIONS.
FOR DETAILS CONTACT GENERAL ENQUIRIES BY TELEPHONE:
+44 (0) 1243 771107, OR EMAIL: ENQUIRIES@SUMMERSDALE.COM

52 THINGS TO DOODLE WHILE YOU POO

HUGH JASSBURN

CONTAINS SOME COLOURFUL LANGUAGE

52 THINGS TO DOODLE...

THE ANCIENT ART OF DOODLING HAS BEEN AROUND FOR THOUSANDS OF YEARS. DEPICTIONS OF WILD BEASTS ON CAVE WALLS, FUNNY LITTLE CARVINGS ON AGE-OLD ARTEFACTS — WE'VE BEEN AT IT A WHILE. SO WHAT BETTER WAY TO CELEBRATE THIS TIME-HONOURED TRADITION THAN BY DOODLING WHILE YOU DUMP? FILL A FISH TANK, ILLUSTRATE THE ALPHABET, ENVISION OUTER SPACE — WHATEVER TAKES YOUR CREATIVE FANCY. SIT BACK, RELAX AND PREPARE TO MAKE YOUR MASTERPIECE...

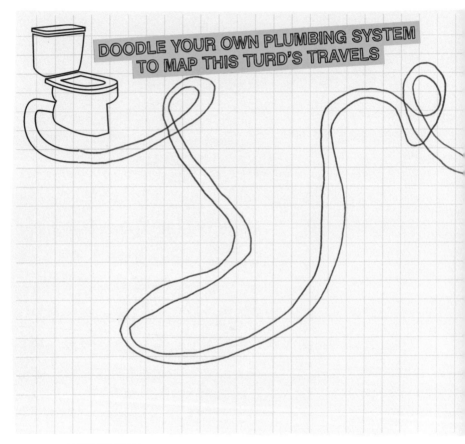

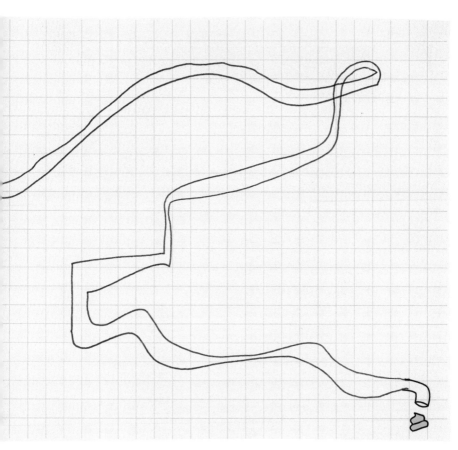

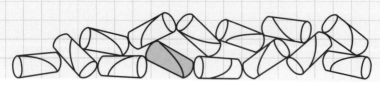

DOODLE A SCENT
TO SUPPRESS YOUR STENCH

SHIT

SHIT

SHIT

and
-ere

WHAT HAS THIS ROLL OF TOILET PAPER
WRAPPED ITSELF AROUND?
DOODLE THE CHAOS

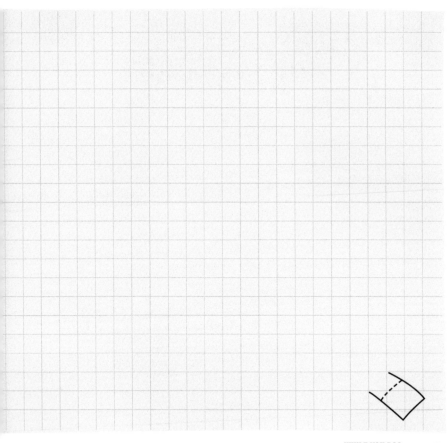

DOODLE A DREAM

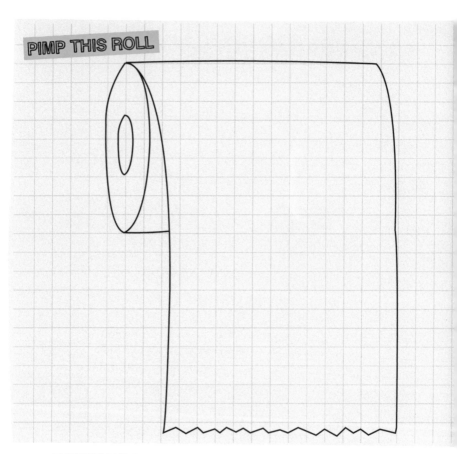

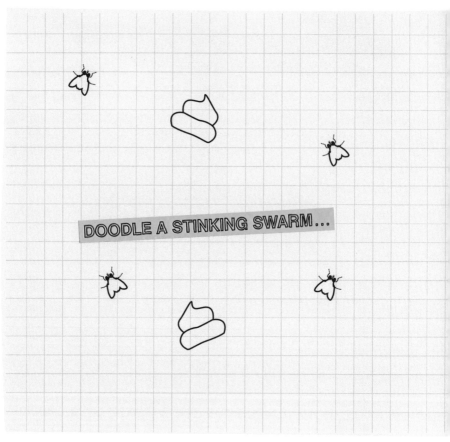

DOODLE A STINKING SWARM...

... OF TURD-TASTING FLIES

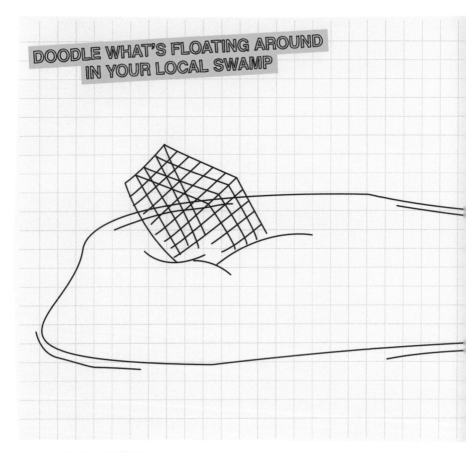

DOODLE WHAT'S FLOATING AROUND
IN YOUR LOCAL SWAMP

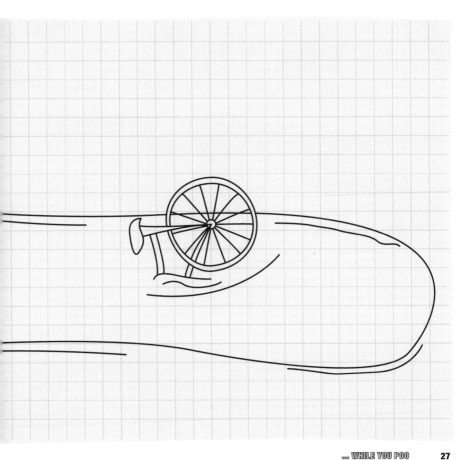

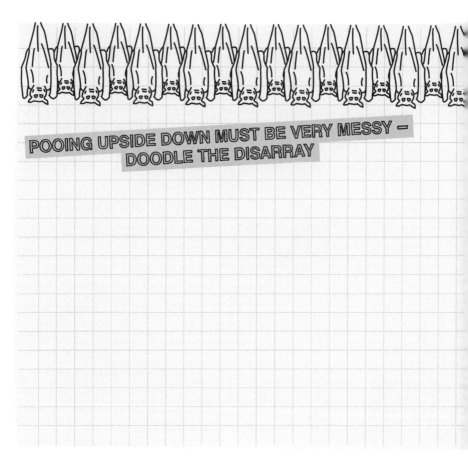

POOING UPSIDE DOWN MUST BE VERY MESSY – DOODLE THE DISARRAY

IT'S NOT JUST BEARS THAT SHIT IN THE WOODS – DOODLE YOUR OWN WILDLIFE

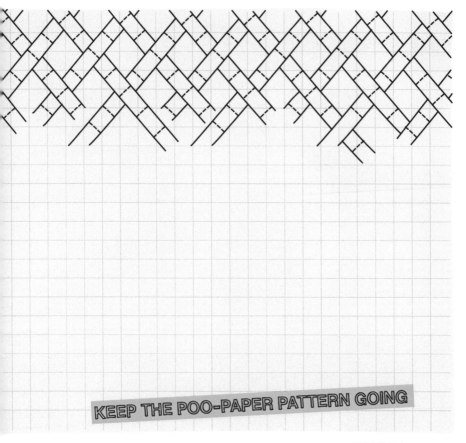

KEEP THE POO-PAPER PATTERN GOING

ANY FLOATERS OUT THERE?

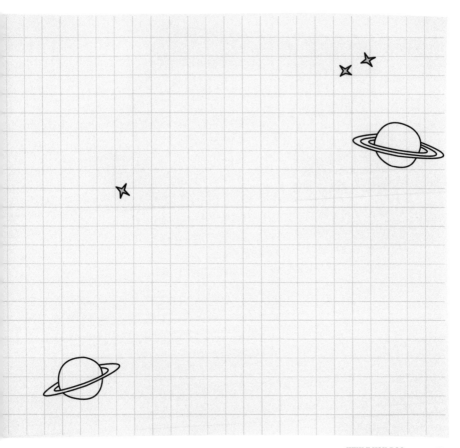

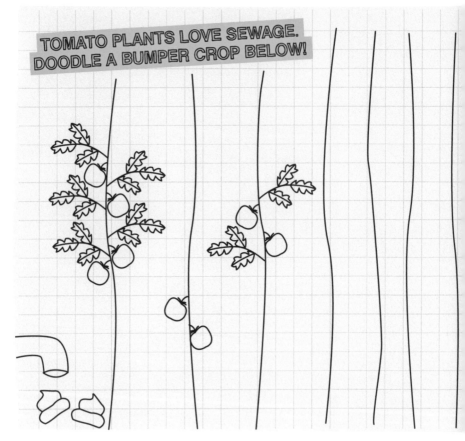

TOMATO PLANTS LOVE SEWAGE. DOODLE A BUMPER CROP BELOW!

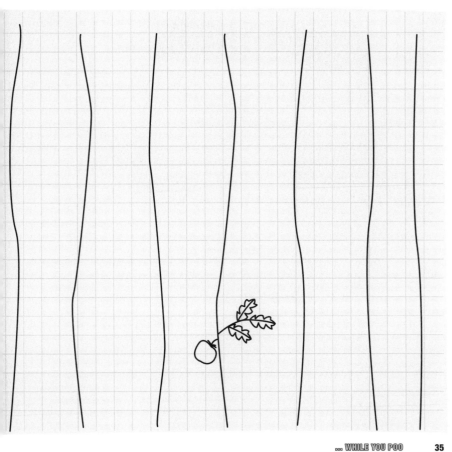

DOODLE THE WORD 'TURD' AND MAKE IT SHINE WITH YOUR DESIGN

DIRECT YOUR OWN SHIT-YOUR-PANTS SCARY MOVIE

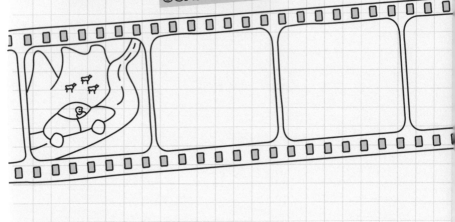

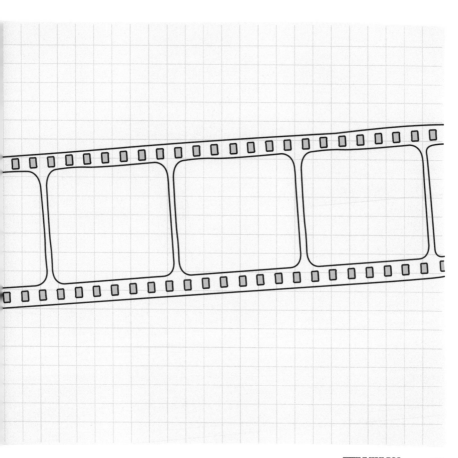

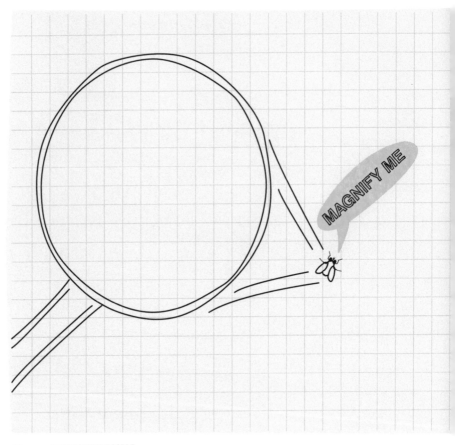

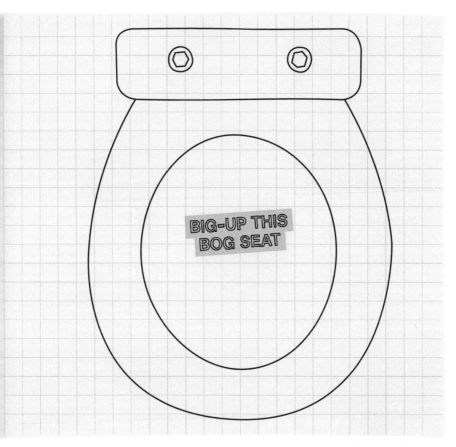

BIG-UP THIS
BOG SEAT

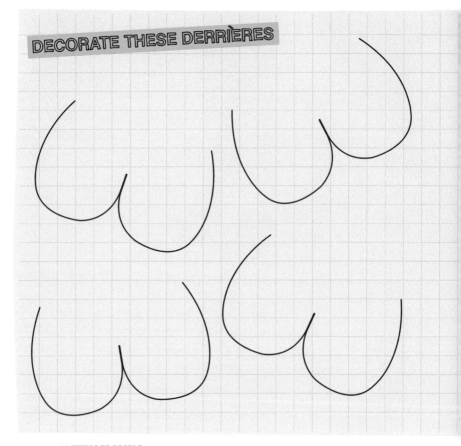

DECORATE THESE DERRIÈRES

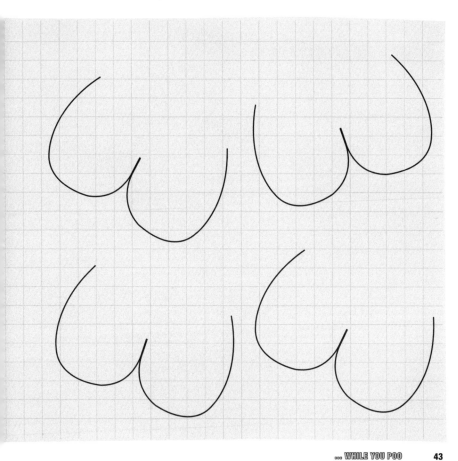

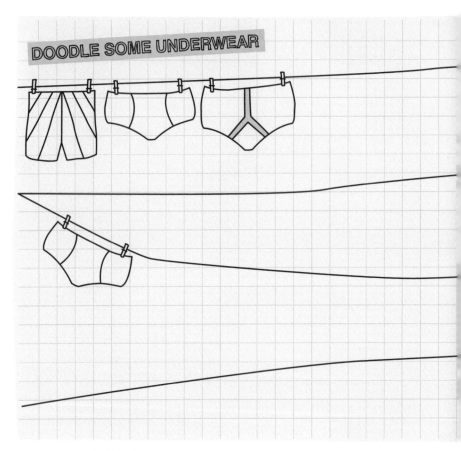

DOODLE SOME UNDERWEAR

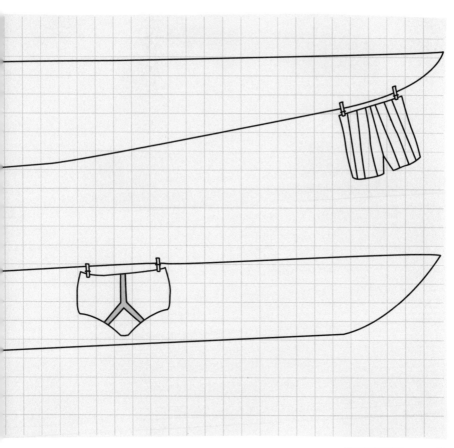

TURDS? CUPCAKES? WHATEVER
– DECORATE THEM

DOODLE A SELF-PORTRAIT WHILE YOU POO

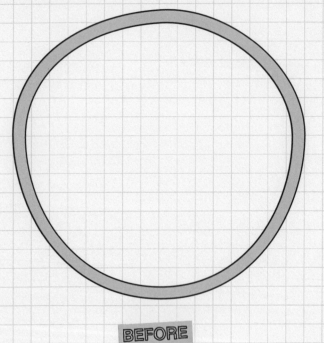

BEFORE

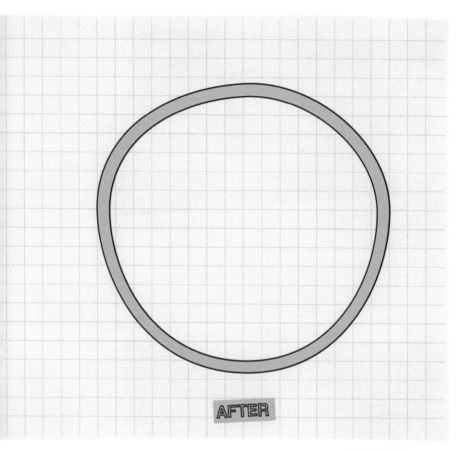

AFTER

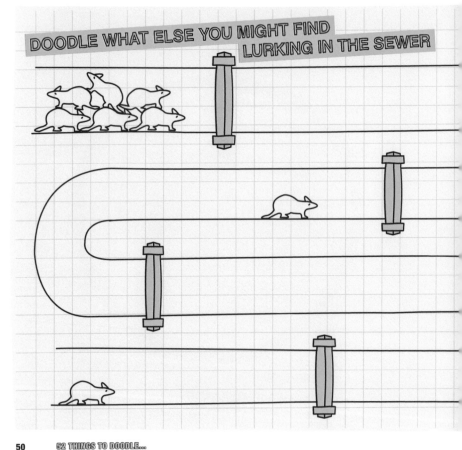

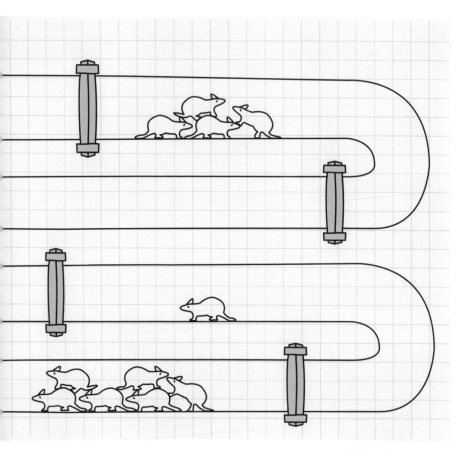

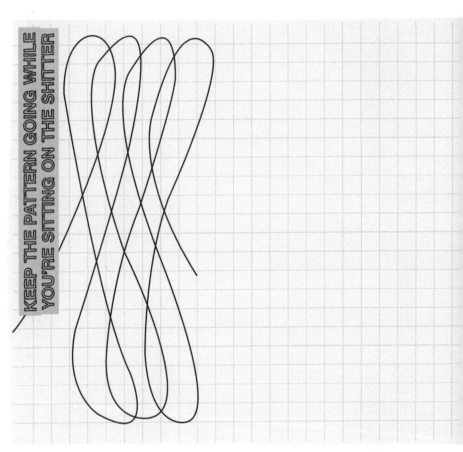

KEEP THE PATTERN GOING WHILE YOU'RE SITTING ON THE SHITTER

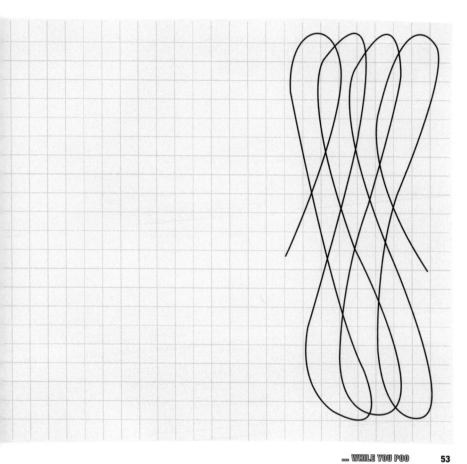

EVERY POSH POWDER ROOM NEEDS SOME PLANTS...

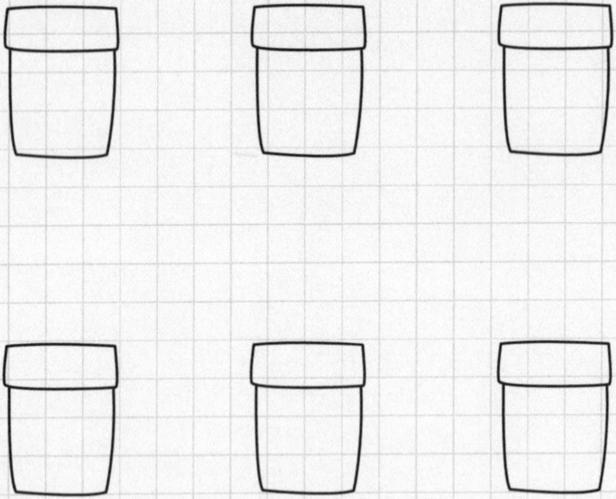

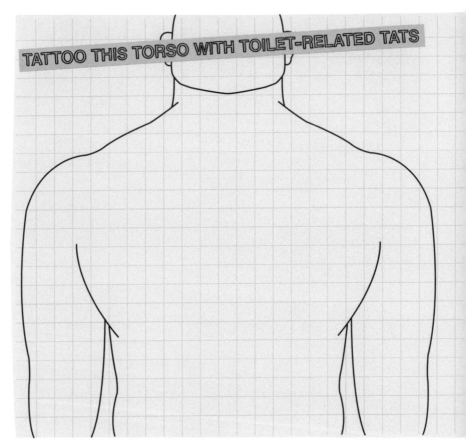

TATTOO THIS TORSO WITH TOILET-RELATED TATS

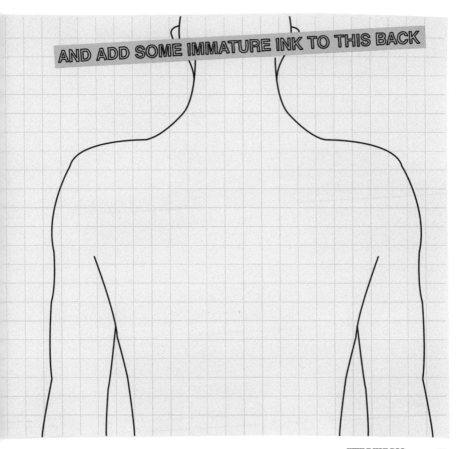

AND ADD SOME IMMATURE INK TO THIS BACK

DOODLE THE WORD 'DUMP' IN YOUR
FAVOURITE FONT AND GET DECORATING

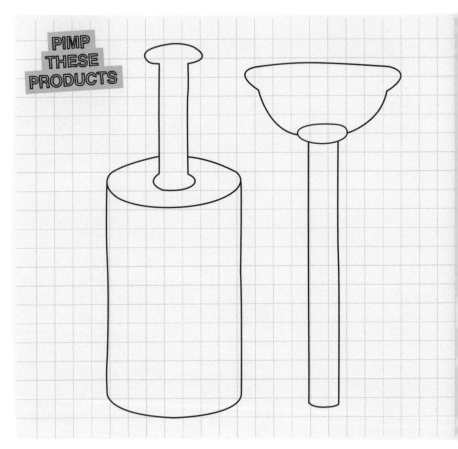

PIMP
THESE
PRODUCTS

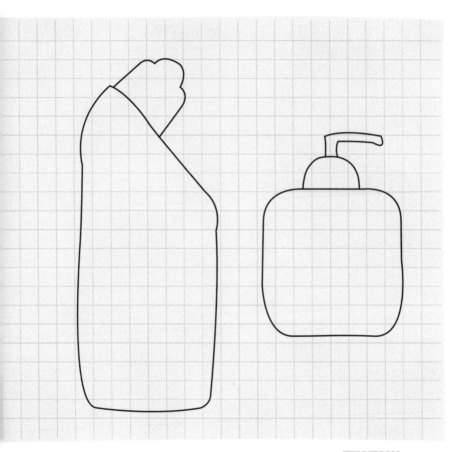

NO SEWAGE IN HERE – JUST FISH

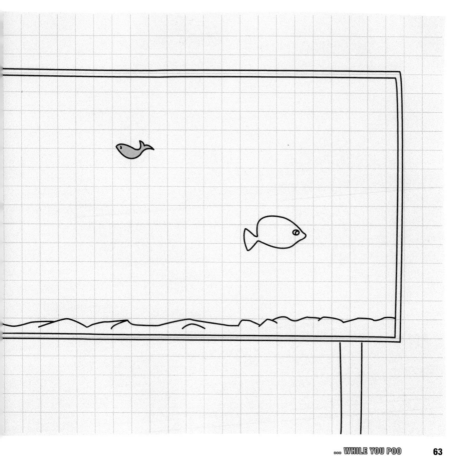

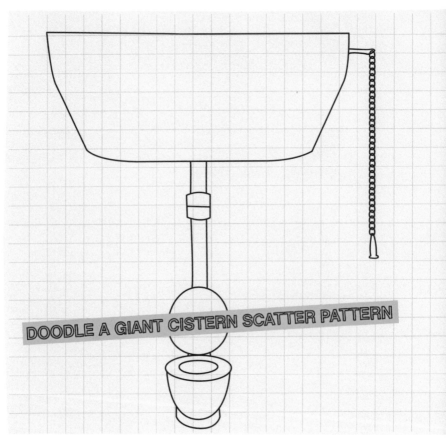

DOODLE A GIANT CISTERN SCATTER PATTERN

DOODLE SOME FIBROUS FOODS THAT GET YOU GOING

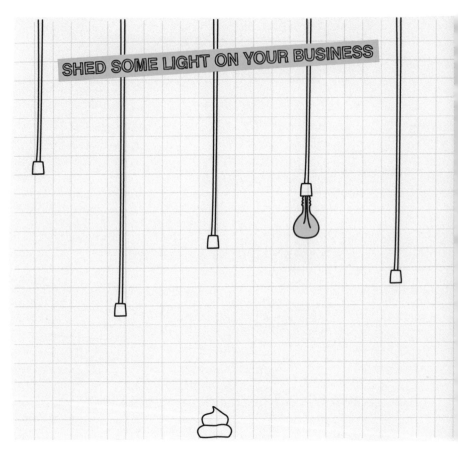

SHED SOME LIGHT ON YOUR BUSINESS

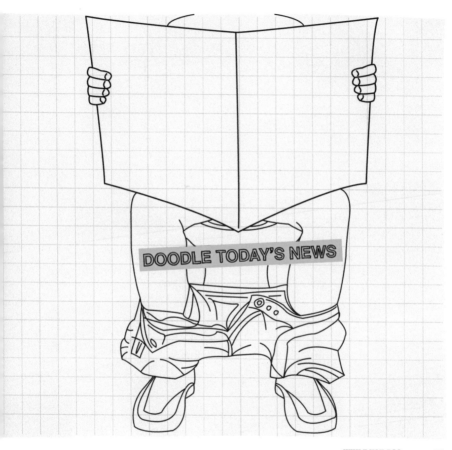

DOODLE TODAY'S NEWS

DOODLE ON THESE DOOR SIGNS

DOODLE SOME POOING FACES

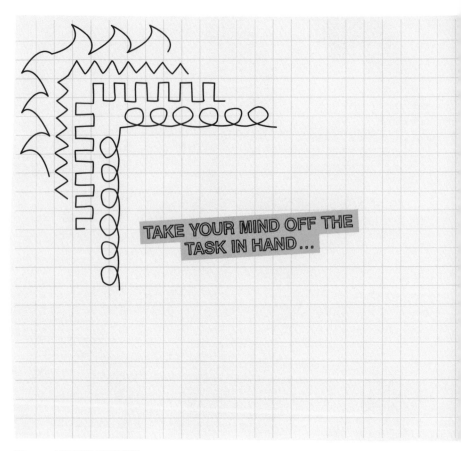

TAKE YOUR MIND OFF THE
TASK IN HAND...

...AND COMPLETE THESE PATTERNS

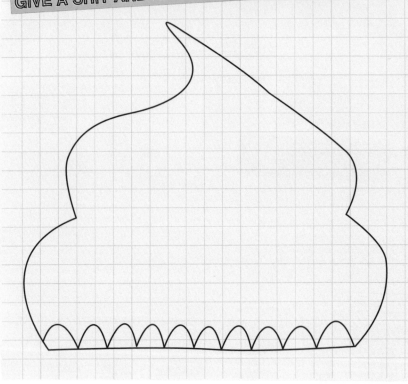

GIVE A SHIT AND EMBELLISH THIS BEAUTY

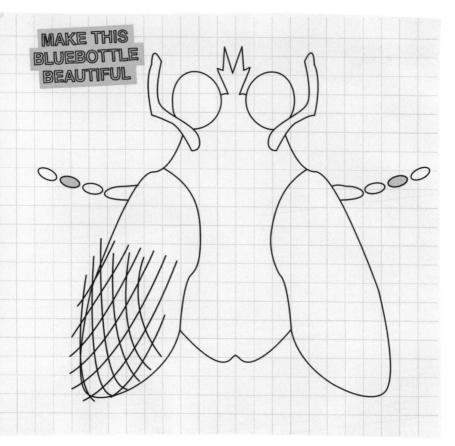

MAKE THIS BLUEBOTTLE BEAUTIFUL

DESIGN MORE CROWNS FOR THE OCCUPANT OF THE PORCELAIN THRONE

DOODLE FIVE THINGS YOU CAN SEE RIGHT NOW

POO, THE MOST NATURAL FERTILIZER —
SHOW HOW THEY GROW

A

B

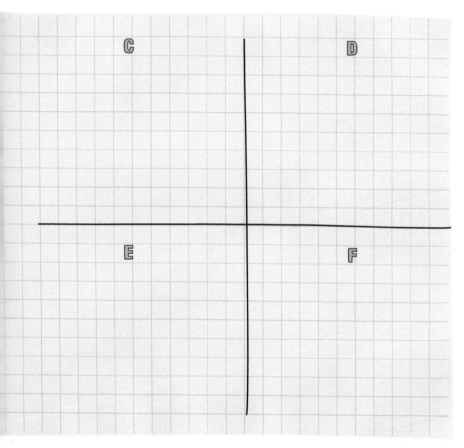

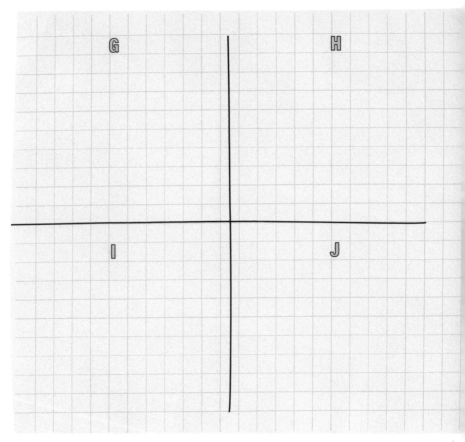

G

H

I

J

K

L

M

N

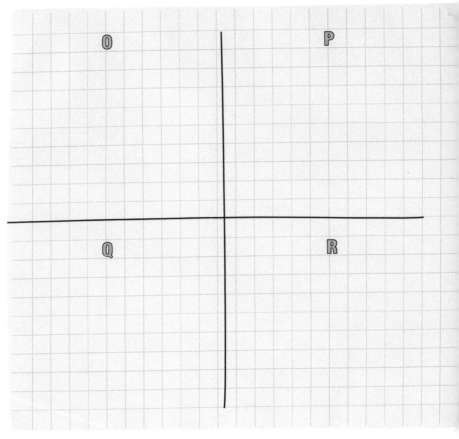

O

P

Q

R

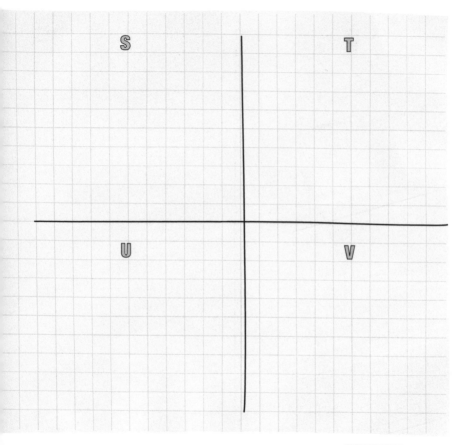

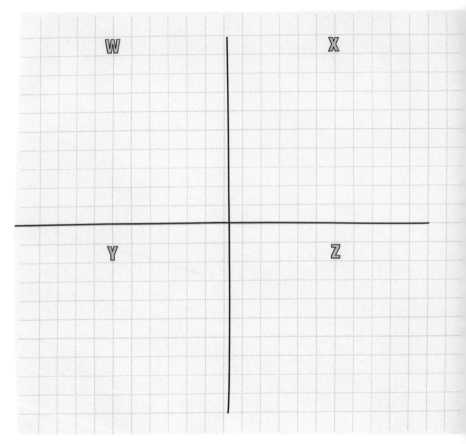

DOODLE YOUR FAVOURITE WORD FOR POO

DOODLE DECORATIONS FOR THIS PORCELAIN COLLECTION

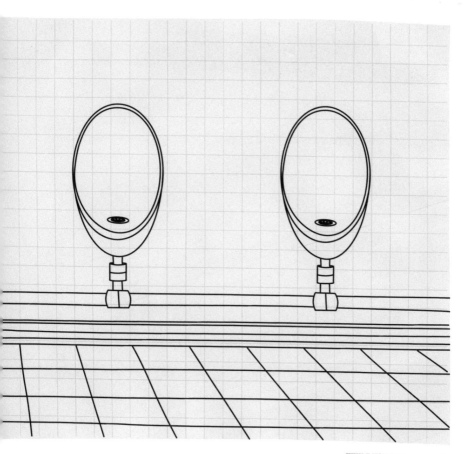

MODERN ART IS CRAP
– MAKE YOUR OWN MASTERPIECES HERE

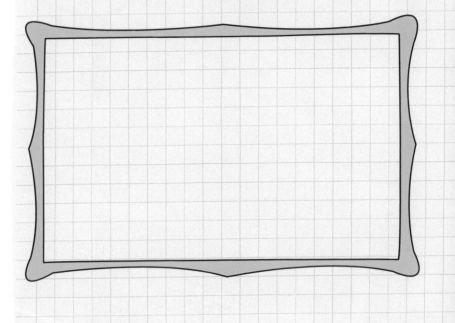

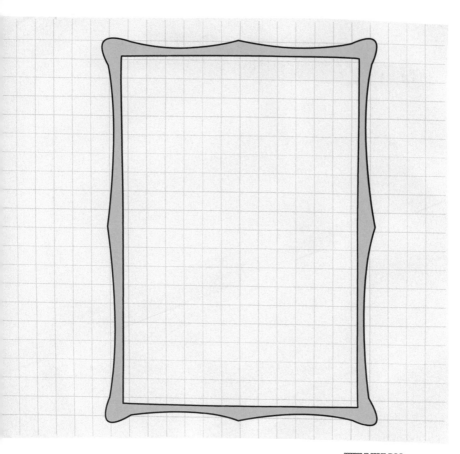

DOODLE THE WORD 'CRAP' AND GET CREATIVE WITH YOUR CREATION

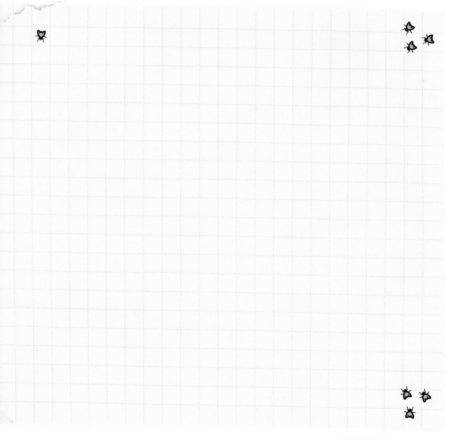

DOODLE WHAT'S IN YOUR U-BEND

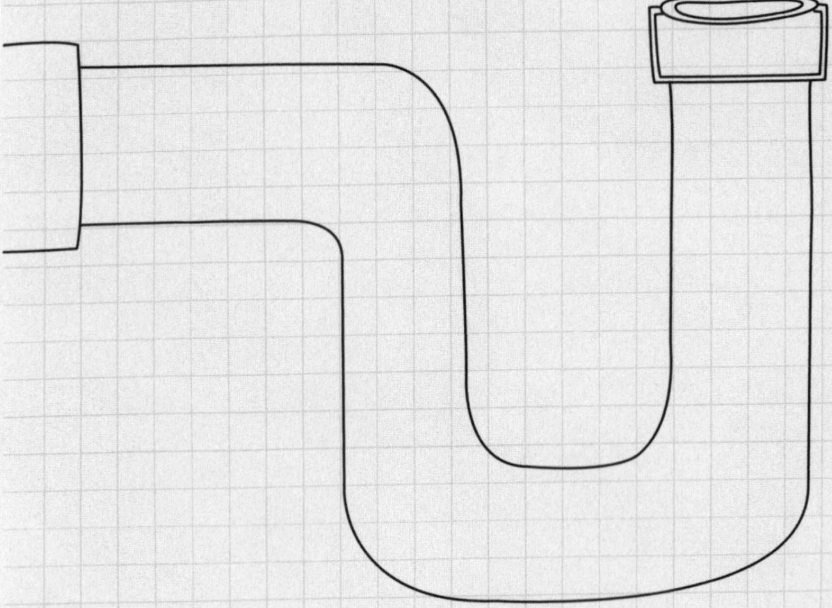

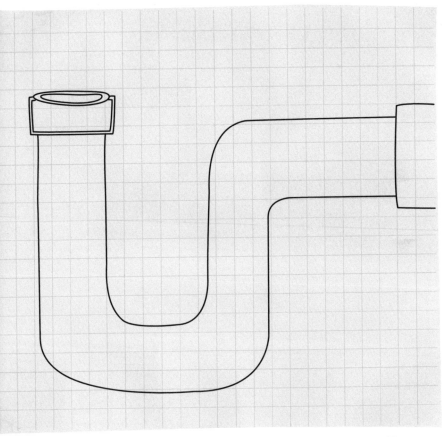

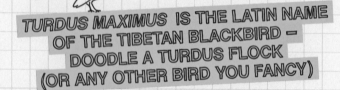

TURDUS MAXIMUS IS THE LATIN NAME
OF THE TIBETAN BLACKBIRD –
DOODLE A TURDUS FLOCK
(OR ANY OTHER BIRD YOU FANCY)

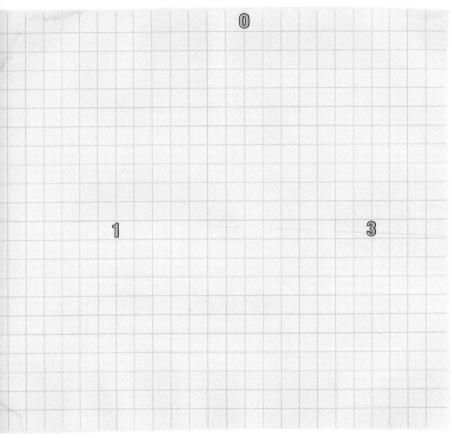

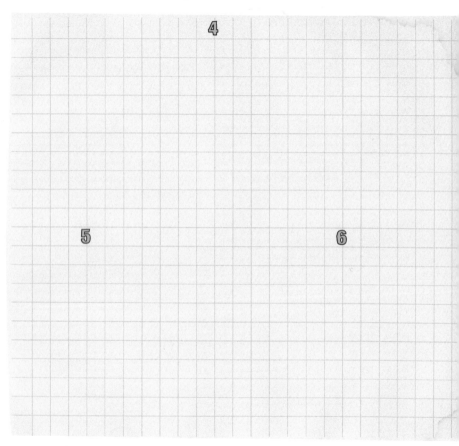

4

5

6

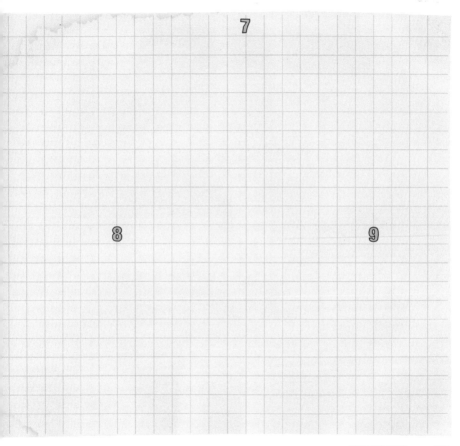

7

8

9

OUTSIDE BOGS ARE FULL OF THEM –
COMPLETE THIS WEB

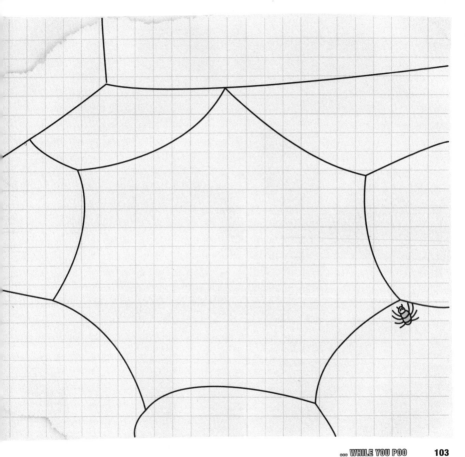

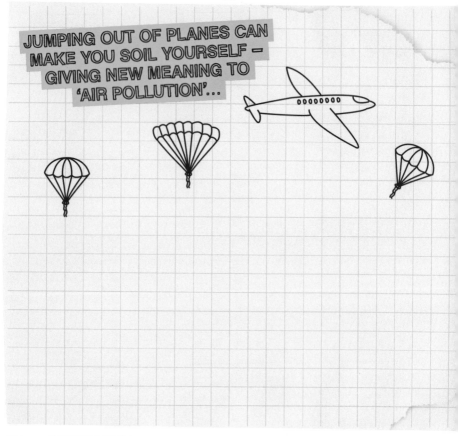

JUMPING OUT OF PLANES CAN MAKE YOU SOIL YOURSELF – GIVING NEW MEANING TO 'AIR POLLUTION'...

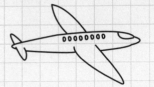
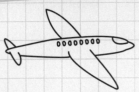

DOODLE ON KITTY AND FILL HER LITTER TRAY

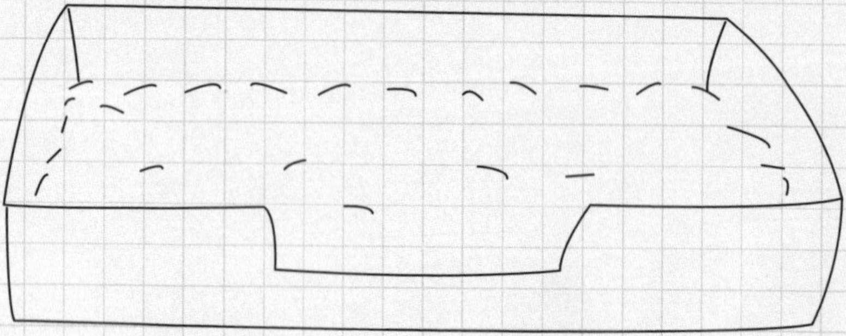

DOODLE ON THESE
DOOR SIGNS

WE SPEND ON AVERAGE THREE YEARS
ON THE TOILET DURING OUR LIFETIME –
LONG ENOUGH TO GROW A VERY
IMPRESSIVE BEARD OR HAIRSTYLE.
DOODLE SOME!

IF YOU'RE INTERESTED IN FINDING OUT MORE ABOUT OUR BOOKS, FIND US ON FACEBOOK AT SUMMERSDALE PUBLISHERS AND FOLLOW US ON TWITTER AT @SUMMERSDALE.

WWW.SUMMERSDALE.COM